As the Crow Flies
A FIRST BOOK OF MAPS

by Gail Hartman
illustrated by Harvey Stevenson

SILVER BURDETT GINN

Needham, MA   Parsippany, NJ
Atlanta, GA   Deerfield, IL   Irving, TX   Santa Clara, CA

SILVER BURDETT GINN
A Division of Simon & Schuster
160 Gould Street
Needham Heights, MA 02194-2310

The text of this book is set in Souvenir Light. The illustrations are rendered
in pen and ink and watercolor. Typography by Julie Quan and Christy Hale

Simon & Schuster edition, 1996

1 2 3 4 5 6 7 8 9 10 SP 01 00 99 98 97 96 95

ISBN : SSB 0–663–59140–6
BSB 0–663–59123–6

AS THE EAGLE SOARS

From the mountains, a stream flows

through a meadow

where a tall tree stands.

mountains

stream

tree

meadow

THE EAGLE'S MAP

A path winds around a farmhouse,

8

past a shed,

to a garden where the sweet greens grow.

garden

shed

farmhouse

my house

THE RABBIT'S MAP

11

AS THE CROW FLIES

A road runs through fields,

past the factory,

to city streets lined with houses.

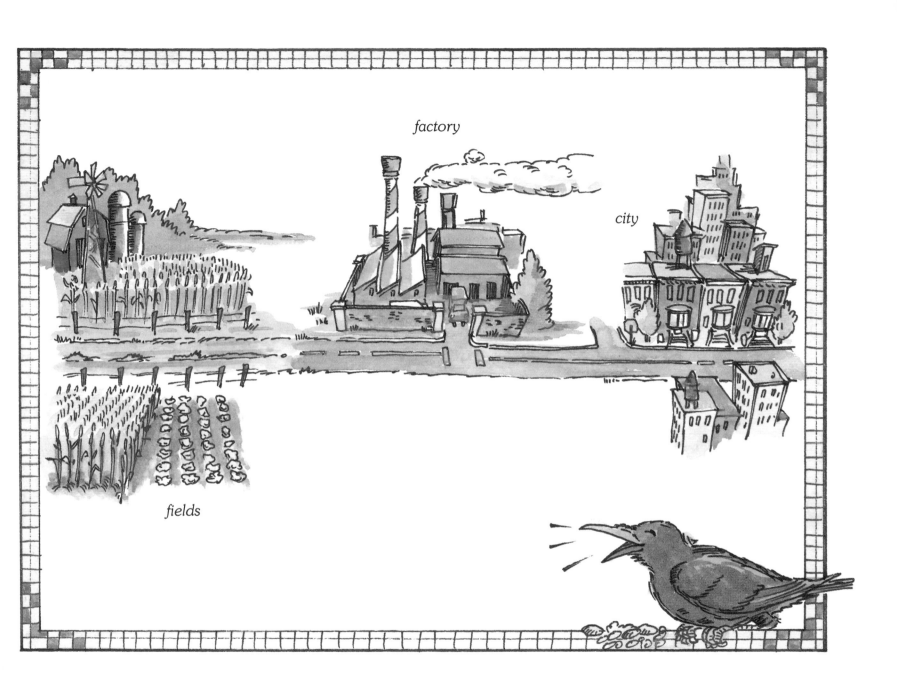

THE CROW'S MAP

AS THE HORSE TROTS

In the city, past the hot dog stand

and skyscrapers,

there is a park where music and the
sounds of children playing fill the air.

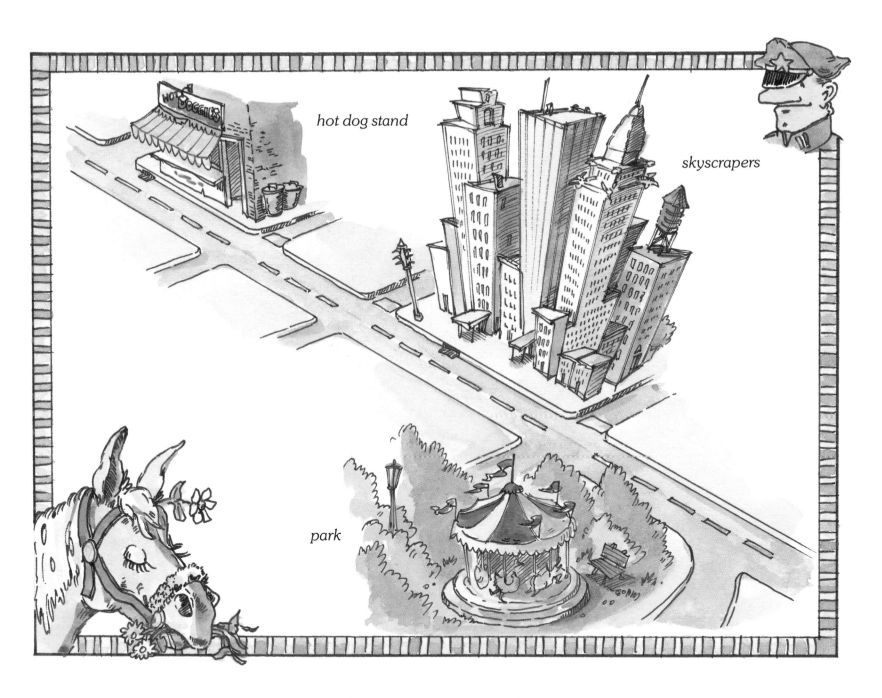

hot dog stand

skyscrapers

park

THE HORSE'S MAP

19

Beyond the fishing boats in the harbor,

near the red brick lighthouse,

the ocean laps the shores of an island.

lighthouse

ocean

harbor

island

THE GULL'S MAP

When the moon shines, it shines on
the shores of the island in the ocean.

It shines on the park

and the houses in the city.

It shines on the garden near
the farmhouse in the country

and on the tree in the meadow,

near mountains that touch the sky.

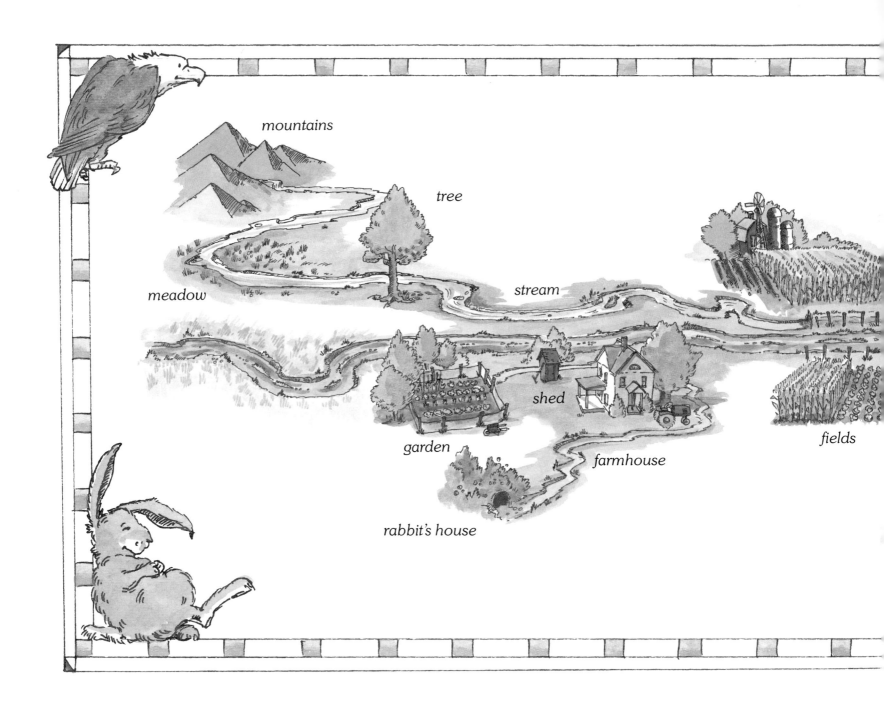

mountains

tree

meadow

stream

shed

garden

fields

farmhouse

rabbit's house

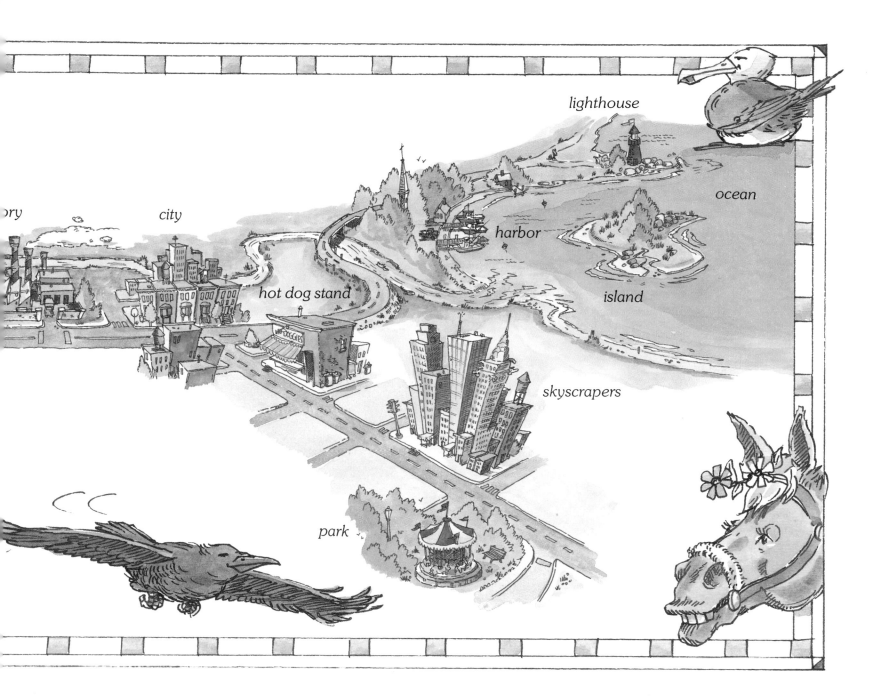

lighthouse

ocean

city

harbor

island

hot dog stand

skyscrapers

park

THE BIG MAP